KEEPING
HENS
IN YOUR GARDEN

A Kitchen Garden Book

Text © Francine Raymond
Illustrations © Gabrielle Stoddart

By the same Author.
In the same series:
Food from the Kitchen Garden
Beekeeping for Beginners (with P. Hands)
Keeping a few Ducks in your Garden
A Peacock on the Lawn (with S. Carpenter)
Goose on the Green
Start your own Garden Farm (with K. Nethercott)
Keeping a Couple of Pigs in your Garden (with K. Nethercott)
Also:
The Big Book of Garden Hens
A Henkeeper's Journal
A Christmas Journal
All my Eggs in one Basket

Published by the Kitchen Garden 1998
Church Lane, Troston
Bury St Edmunds Suffolk IP31 1EX
Tel 01359 268 322
Email: francine@kitchen-garden-hens.co.uk
www.kitchen-garden-hens.co.uk

ISBN 0-9532857-1-5

Printed in England on recycled paper

The Talmud, on the compatibility of hens and gardens:
*"If one sees a cockerel in a dream, he may expect a son;
if several cocks - several sons; if a hen - a fine garden
and rejoicing."*

Introduction

For the past 15 years I've been keeping a few hens and a cockerel in my garden in Suffolk. The birds are happy and supply my family with delicious eggs, the garden is well manured and flourishes, and the chickens give us real pleasure. I have many friends who keep poultry and hope this book will encourage you to do the same.

I suggest a simple system: that you buy two or three hens and keep them in a henhouse with a run and as much access to your garden as you can. I can guarantee fun for all, and if you are prepared to set aside ten minutes a day and as much space as you can spare, you'll reap rich rewards. This apart, you need just a little common sense and to stick to a few basic principles.

You'll all learn a lot form raising hens naturally and they'll help improve the ecosystem in your garden. Plants and animals will produce to their full potential, your hens eating kitchen and garden scraps and in return providing eggs for you and fertilizer for the plants. Children love to be involved and to collect eggs, a pleasure that perhaps dims with time and adolescence - but for small visitors it is always a big treat.

Why not keep a pure breed pair or trio for interest and glamour, plus a hybrid or crossbreed for a constant supply of eggs? You don't need a cockerel's involvement for your hens to produce eggs. The male of the species is the more striking, but not recommended for beginners. Mine looks after his ladies very well, keeping an eye open and calling if he finds some delicious morsel. By keeping the rare breeds you'll help to ensure the future of these beautiful birds and retain the valuable free-range habits and characteristics that have been lost in their relations crammed in battery cages. Agricultural history will applaud you.

Starting out can be bewildering. Neighbourly advice, books full of anatomical detail, diseases and practices that you or I would consider cruel will put you off. Most publications assume you have a degree in agriculture, acres of land and ambitions to supply eggs to Sainsbury's. Keeping hens in your garden does not have to be complicated. Most fowl problems are caused by stress, overcrowded conditions and lack of tender loving care. I hope what follows will de-mystify the situation

Where to begin.

If you like the idea of a few hens in your garden, there are decisions to make and practical steps to take. First contact your Environmental Health Officer at the Town Hall to check if there are any contra-indications to your keeping poultry in the local bylaws. You may be curtailed if you live in a built-up area.

Next and most importantly, you must talk to your neighbours to see if they will help if you're away and are prepared to put up with the noise (not much if you stick to hens only). If you want to keep a cockerel, the crowing could be a worry. My husband was distinctly wary, but now says he doesn't notice the early morning alarm calls. There are, in fact a few solutions to the problem in the next chapter. When you have dealt with these matters, decide where to site your chicken run. Choose a place as sheltered from the wind, as spacious, secure and as close to the house as possible. Your birds' main enemies are uncontrolled dogs and of course, foxes. If you live in a very foxy area, try doves instead. It's not worth the heartbreak - or the expense.

On to expense. Assuming you decide on two or three hens you can expect to pay little more than a couple of pounds a week on feed, depending on how free-range your birds are and how much surplus pasta and rice you cook. Your *palais de poulets* can cost as little or as much as you want. There is a design you could copy in the next chapters and there are several books on DIY henhouse building.

You could use an existing shed provided it is draughtproof (but well-ventilated at the apex), waterproof and secure. Alternatively you can contact one of the companies listed at the back of this book and send for their catalogues. Henhouses can be painted to fit into your garden colour scheme and made to look as exotic and witty as you like. Feel free to try Gothic, Moorish, Post Modern or Queen Anne.

Finding your hens will be great fun. Look locally first. Try asking feed merchants, and vets. Go to shows and read the local press. Don't buy from markets, no one ever sends their best birds to market. You'll make some good contacts and meet some fascinating people: small-scale breeders who will convince you of the charms of their particular fancies, after having vetted you as a suitable owner. Give yourself plenty of time, you may have to order and wait for eggs to hatch or chicks to grow.

If nothing comes up then write to one of the suppliers of pure breeds on my list in the address section. Always visit before buying. To help you to decide, I describe eight recommended varieties in the chapter on Breeds.

Finally, although I hope to convince you that keeping hens is easy, remember that they must be visited twice a day, and cleaned out at least once a week. This doesn't take long - just a few minutes a day - but beware, it can develop into a consuming passion.

Where to keep your hens.
The ideal site is a small sheltered, sunny orchard, or a fenced woodland grove. Probably you won't have either. Neither do I. My hens live in an eight metre square run, fenced with two metre high bird-proof chicken wire, camouflaged with climbing plants for extra shelter. To one side, there is an area which is roofed with rigid plastic, so that the flock can be fed under cover. The bottom six inches of netting are dug into the ground to stop tunnelling predators. The run has a self-closing gate.

Within the run, to one side, out of the wind, sits the henhouse - a bit like the one overleaf. Painted the same terracotta and sage green as our house, it has an Onduline roof and is functional and pretty - there is something very appealing about small-scale houses. The chickens roost upstairs at night, underneath to shelter from the rain, and stay inside its wired confines for breakfast, before I let them out into the run.

The stylish American writer Martha Stewart has covered her henhouse with painted trellis and grows climbers all over it. She also trains roses on the surrounding fence, and these benefit form the extra fertilizer. Some people let their hens out into the garden to range free in the afternoon when they come home from work. The troupe will make their own way back to roost as the light fades, because hens can't see in the dark. The space you give your birds depends on how much garden you are prepared to give up and your commitments outside the home. I plead the maximum free-range possible depending on the vulnerability of your plants and the risk to your hens from predators should you be out.

Inside the henhouse I line the roosting area with newspaper and use dust-free chopped straw as bedding, which rots down well on the compost heap. You will need to clean the quarters weekly and give a complete disinfecting with Antex or Jeyes fluid occasionally. In early Spring, I confine my hens and while they are *in situ*, I dig over their run bit by bit. They are kept busy scratching for worms while my vegetables grow unimpaired. You will also need to keep your hens in a coop when they first arrive, letting them out into the run after a day or two, then out for the first time into the garden, just before bedtime.

Two methods can control the early crowing loved by some but not by all. Your cockerel may be fooled if your henhouse is completely lightproof, but remember, it must still be well ventilated for the health of its residents. Also if the cockerel is confined to a top roost he may be unable to stretch into crowing position.

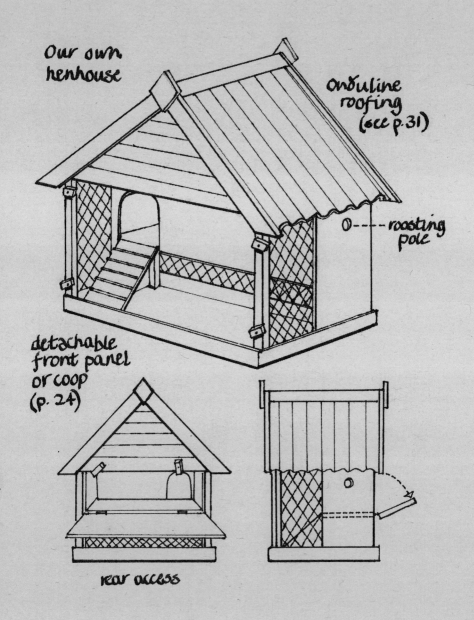

Our own
henhouse

onduline
roofing
(see p.31)

o----roosting
pole

detachable
front panel
or coop
(p. 24)

rear access

11

Which breed?

All domestic chickens originate from the Jungle Fowl that range the tropical forests of Asia but the variety of their descendants is truly amazing. You can choose from hundreds of breeds of chickens. Some traditional backyard birds, like the Rhode Island Red or English Light Sussex are easy, amiable and widely available, but generally: the better the layer - the more damage they do in the garden. Other pure breeds are extraordinarily colourful and expensive and not a good idea for beginners, but if eventually you do progress to a rare breed, you have the added advantage of knowing you are encouraging an endangered species.

Start with two or three birds, you can always get a few more next year, thus prolonging your egg supplies. You could also get a farmyard crossbreed, not as elegant, but like mongrels, they often carry the best traits and make good layers. Chickens come in two sizes, bantam or full size. I prefer big birds because they tend to be more docile, and less noisy, but for a really small garden, a pair of pretty bantams is ideal. A bantam can live for five years, larger fowl for up to ten. The more free range your hens are, the longer they'll live.

I recommend the following breeds from my own and friends' experience, at prices up to £30 per bird. Whatever you choose, go and see them before you buy, checking the birds are healthy and have been well looked after. My choices are displayed on centrefolds overleaf in all their glory with their vital statistics.

Pekin (China)

A pretty bantam with feathered feet that supposedly scratches less in the garden. They are gentle, excellent sitters and require little space. A wonderful range of colours: black, blue, lavender, buff, white; also partridge, cuckoo and mottled. Highly recommended, especially for children.

Orpington (GB)

Large, docile and tame, beloved of the Queen Mother (and myself). A good table bird, but eating your Orpington would be like dining on the family Labrador. Fairly chatty. Beautiful feathers, available in several solid colours: buff, black, blue and white. Often broody, lays surprisingly small tinted eggs.

Rhode Island Red (USA)
The traditional-looking chocolate brown hens that lays lots of tinted eggs. A good forager (so perhaps not such a good idea for sensitive gardeners) and long lived, this utility bird is bright, alert and quiet. An old Rhody makes a good family pet.

Silkie (Asia)
A small breed that makes an excellent broody on any eggs. Available in various plain colours with silly little pom-pom on their head. Soft, with really silky hair-like feathers, a charming bird to keep as a pet.

Sussex (GB)
Very old and popular breed. The Light Sussex has a black and white neck and tail, but also comes in buff, brown, speckled, silver and white. Good backyard fowl, laying tinted eggs. A friend who has always kept them says she has 'never known a nasty one.'

Brahma (India)
The gentle giant of the hen world, sedate, quiet and easy to handle. Lays brown eggs and makes a good mum. Copes well with cold weather. Beautifully pencilled feathers that cover legs. Light, dark, gold, buff and white. Dressed by Armani.

Plymouth Rock (USA)

Prolific layers of brown eggs. Solid, plump and strong, the Barred Rocks look like Victorian bathers in stripy costumes. The most beautiful markings I've seen, but also available in plain buff, white, black and the rare Colombian.

Farmyard Crossbreed

Good layer, docile and unfazed, makes a perfect companion to a pair of pure breeds. Good value and hardy, a beginner's hen. Some combinations are lovely. Commercial hybrids are over-enthusiastic gardeners and not designed for longevity, just regular egg production.

What to feed your hens.
Hens are omnivores and need a basic diet of grain, (in the form of mixed corn) and protein which you buy as mash or pellets. These fundamentals are naturally supplemented with insects and worms (and you hope, slugs and snails) from the garden, green stuff from the kitchen or grass from the surroundings. The more free-range your birds are, the less food you have to supply. Water must be available at all times. They also need grit, which they pick up from the soil to enable them to digest the food in their crop. Birds are very efficient at balancing their own nutritional requirements.

You can get your supplies from a local feed merchant - look in Yellow Pages under Animal Foodstuffs. Try always to buy non-animal based feed. Allen and Page produce a range of poultry food approved by the Vegetarian Society. (See back page for stockists and mail order). Your merchant will sell chopped straw for bedding, straw bales for shelter, kibbled maize for broodies, chick crumbs, and flint grit for making sound eggshells. He will be a useful source of information too

Chickens, like children, thrive on routine, so develop one that suits you all and stick to it. In the morning, I feed mine their breakfast of moistened brown bread, sunflower hearts and protein pellets, in the covered part of the run. Make sure there is fresh water. In the evening (or late afternoon in Winter) I place a large dish of mixed corn - a slowly digested supper - in the run, which can be removed at bedtime to discourage vermin. Special galvanized food and drink containers can be bought from farm shops and suppliers, including a useful automatic feeder.

Keep your sacks of grain and pellets in small, galvanized dustbins with metal lids. This deters rats and mice. Buy only one sack of each at a time, so that your hens' feed is always fresh. In winter you may feel your birds are short of the greenery they need. If so, put some lettuce, cabbage or spinach leaves - mine love sorrel - in an old string bag and hang it over them in the run.

For treats, hens love fruit and pips, sunflower seeds, hard cheese, cooked pasta and rice, peas and sweetcorn. Use these bits to tame your birds. You'll feel bucolic contentment as they come and eat from your hand. Never give them citrus fruit, salt, meat, fish or anything that isn't fresh. Clear up any leftover food because hens are very messy eaters.

Eggs and Chicks

If you order your birds in the Spring, they should be ready to collect in late Summer. They may already be producing eggs if they are more than 20-24 weeks old. Hens normally lay from Valentine's Day through to Guy Fawkes, though some will produce all year round yielding three to six eggs a week.

The egg is a perfect natural food; unrefined, unprocessed, unenriched - and free-range eggs definitely taste better, believe me. The most versatile ingredient in your larder, you can keep them for up to three weeks, but the joy of owning hens is being able to eat really fresh eggs. Depending on your breed, you will get brown, tinted, white speckled or even turquoise blue eggs. Clean them immediately with a moist cloth or a piece of loofah. Don't soak them in water because the shells are porous.

After you have been keeping hens for a while, and assuming you have a cockerel, you may decide to augment your flock by rearing a few chicks from eggs in the Spring. This can happen without your intervention and you may have already been presented with a *fait accompli* if you hens are truly free-range. If you want to try a new breed or don't have a cockerel, you can buy fertile eggs of any variety from a breeder to hatch at home. Only increase your flock by two or three at a time.

What you need is a broody. You may have noticed a hen that sits all day in the nestbox, fluffs up clucking and reacts angrily, even pecking if you disturb her. If you don't want chicks, remove any eggs she lays and shut her out of the nestbox. It may take several days, but persist. She'll give up eventually. If you do want chicks, go back to the nest in the evening. Quietly and carefully, move the broody to a strong cardboard box (open at the base directly on to the earth with a little straw around the edge to form a hollow) in a quiet place away from the flock. Put the box into a coop (see page 24). Place any eggs you want to hatch under her, but don't let her sit on more eggs than you want chicks.

Every day, at the same time, take her out and make sure she eats, drinks and performs her ablutions. She will protest. The incubation period is 21 days from the time she started sitting. When the chicks hatch, they will stay under their mother for a couple of days. When they appear, offer them some chick crumbs sprinkled on the ground and water in a shallow, untippable dish. She will show them what to do, your role is supervisory. Keep an eye on the other hens though, especially when you let mum and chicks into the main run, and don't let them into the broody coop.

This way of increasing your flock by one or two birds is great fun, especially for children. In nature though, nothing is guaranteed and you could end up with surplus cockerels that will fight. You may be lucky and find a home for a good pure breed, but chances are, extra males will have to be culled, it's a problem worth considering before you start.

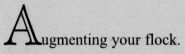ugmenting your flock.

For a continuing supply of eggs, increase your flock by a couple of hens every year or so. Hatching out your own chicks is the most natural way to build up stock; the newcomers are introduced gradually as they grow and can be released from the run at about six weeks. My little troupe have always shown a communal interest in the broody's offspring and I have never had trouble, but Nellie is top hen and fiercer than a tiger protecting her babes.

Chicks can be bought at twelve weeks old, but without a minder they have to be raised in a separate run until they can hold their own. Alternatively buy at point of lay (20-24 weeks). Whatever aged birds you bring in, they must spend several days in *purdah*, cooped inside the run so the other occupants get used to them little by little. It's quite likely they have been kept in a cage by the breeder, and may find your wide-open spaces a little daunting. I think it kinder to buy in pairs, so at least there's one familiar face.

It can take ages for a new bird to be fully accepted, so keep an eye on her to stop any nastiness. If a particular hen is doing the bullying, you could try cooping *her* and letting the victim run with the others. There's always a pecking order in a flock, but with lots of room and other things to do, it should only be a problem at mealtimes. Let the newcomer dine alone for a while.

Below is my husband's design for a coop made from 1" x 2" batten (which could be bought cut to size by a timber merchant). It has been stained and screwed together and then covered and stapled with plastic netting from the garden centre. If you leave part of the un-netted and replace it with a board, this can be removed for access at feeding time and will provide shelter from the rain and sun. This light structure has proved endlessly useful for broodies, patients and new arrivals, and when not in use, it's popped over my vegetable bed to protect my saladini from unwelcome diners

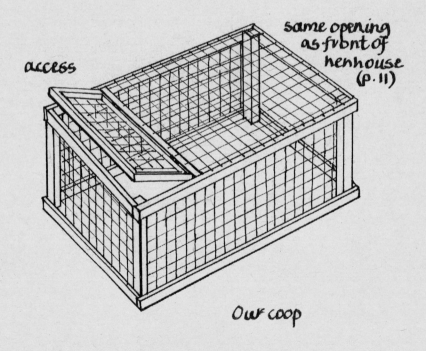

access

same opening as front of henhouse (p. 11)

Our coop

I know it's possible to manage more than one cockerel at a time, especially in a large free-range set-up, but I can't cope with the endless bickering and constant drama. If you run several small flocks, let them sleep in separate henhouses, but remember - the more hens, the bigger the toll they take on your garden. Let the amount of space you can spare govern the number of birds you keep, and not your enthusiasm - or appetite for eggs.

G ardening with hens

I love watching my cockerel as he escorts his motley troupe of ladies round the garden. As a keen gardener, I'm less pleased with the dust craters, pecked new growth and disinterred planting. Over the years I've developed strategies to minimize the problems and I make the most of the undoubted advantages.

Besides being decorative and charming, hens are excellent pest controllers. They are first class weed seed devourers and land clearers. Chicken droppings can be used in the garden in three ways: firstly as a compost activator; secondly, when composted with layers of the hens' bedding material the mixture makes a good soil conditioner; and finally combined with sulphate or murate of potash to make a balanced plant food - droppings are very high in nitrogen and phosphates. Never use the manure fresh or unmixed, as it's too strong and will burn plants, but treated as I suggest, it will enhance the fertility of your garden immeasurably. To disperse messes from a pristine lawn use a besom broom or a quick burst from a high powered hose.

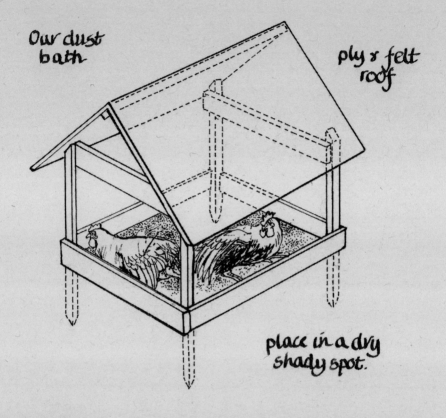

Our dust
bath

ply & felt
roof

place in a dry
shady spot.

In late Spring, I confine my hens in their run in order to protect new growth in the garden. I tip all waste plant material and lawn mowings in with them to scratch through and eat. In July (my garden's low point) they are let out again and vulnerable plants are protected with various cloches. Areas of new planting and the salad bed are covered with permanent low cages or netted. Ideally one would have a walled or fenced kitchen garden or fruit cage and this would also deter rabbits,

27

pigeon and deer. Consider also, the old cottagers' idea of growing vegetables tucked away in the front garden. To prevent unsightly pockmarks from dust bathing, it is wise to provide a perfect dust bath in the run (see opposite). Protect the base of newly planted trees and shrubs by placing large flints or pebbles around their stems.

I actually garden with my hens. They follow me around, darting between my feet for insects as I turn the soil with my trowel. Be patient and leave the freshly dug soil for them to explore before planting the next day and then mulch with mushroom compost (which hens seem to dislike). I always cloche plants till they're established. When I'm sitting on the lawn or kneeling gardening, my hens think I'm a different species to the upright person they usually deal with - an approachable friend.

In Autumn and Winter, keeping poultry is a definite plus in the garden. They forage for pests, finish off old veg and liberally manure the beds. Fallen leaves can be found a use for as a cover for muddy runs or dried and used as bedding. This turns into excellent compost. Domestic fowl create flashes of movement and drama that's so often missing at this time of the year. The henhouse and its occupants provide a valuable splash of the year-round colour and will give you a chnace to show off your decorative flair.

As in all endeavours there will be the odd mishap, but there will also be delicious brown eggs and friendly, beady faces. I promise - it's all worthwhile.

Problems

It's hardly surprising that most poultry problems are caused by stress - due to overcrowding or trauma. Give your birds a peaceful life, plenty of space, adequate food and water and lots to amuse themselves in their own limited way, and you'll be spared most of the ghastly textbook disasters. If however, any bird becomes ill, isolate her in a coop (with access to drinking water) and contact the vet. Your hens will probably have cost more than the family cat. Explain she is a much loved pet and she will be treated as such, though vets that specialize in poultry are as rare as hens' teeth.

If your birds seem off-colour, try a half a teaspoon of Epsom Salts in their drinking water or a dash of cod liver oil with food as a tonic, especially during the moult. All chickens moult annually in late summer. The hens stop laying, cockerels choose not to mate and they all mooch about in various states of undress for about four weeks (the older the hen, the longer the moult). Poultry don't thrive in hot weather. Make sure they are kept in cool, shady, well-ventilated conditions. The henhouse will have to be cleaned more frequently.

Hens may not be the brightest of birds, but treated well they can become endearingly friendly. A persistently aggressive one can be calmed by regular gentle conversation and stroking at dusk in the roost. Some breeds of cockerel, especially game varieties are unpleasantly belligerent. Ask your breeder about the ones to avoid. Sometimes though it's a matter of individual temperament, and with age and patience they may calm down.

When you have to confine your birds to the run, they may be flighty and escape (young birds sometimes do, especially if small and light.) Their wings can be clipped. This may sound drastic but it's not, you are only trimming the first three or four feathers of one wing, and they will grow back. Get someone to help and hold while you cut. Do check that the quills you are snipping are transparent and empty, and do not wing clip during the moult.

If for any reason you have to cull a bird, it's best to call the vet or someone who is experienced. You can't really tell someone how to dispatch a chicken, you have to show them. Probably you will only ever have to do it once, not often enough to learn by practice, and a botched job can be a nightmare for all concerned. With a little luck though, all your birds will live long, happy and productive lives, providing you with delicious eggs, cheerful companionship and enough enthusiasm to try again and again.

Useful Addresses
Forsham Cottage Arks - housing and equipment 01233 820229
Domestic Fowl Trust - breeds - equipment   01386 833083
The Wernlas Collection - breeds   01584 856318
C&J Bird Food - sunflower hearts & mixed corn 01743 709545
Andrew Crace - Bamboo cloches for stockists   01279 842685
Onduline Roofing - stockists   0207 7270533
Allen & Page feed - stockists   01362 822900

The Kitchen Garden Shop - henlovers' paradise is open on Fridays and Saturdays (10 till 5) from Easter Saturday until the end of September. Also for Christmas during the first week in December. Phone to make sure 01359 268 322 or visit our website:- www.kitchen-garden-hens.co.uk

Join the Henkeepers' Association for up-to-date health advice, information and support:- www.henkeepersassociation.co.uk